Group I. Poems expressing a longing
for home or some much
loved place.

1) * West Wind
2) * Lake Isle of Innisfree
3) * Sea Fever
4) Essex
5) * Christmas, 1903
6) Romney Marsh.
7) * He does not die

2. Poems dealing with sea

* 1) Sea Fever
* 2) Marines
* 3) Christmas 1903
* 4) Cargoes
* 5) Flannan Isle.
6) San Stefano
7) Essex
8) Cinque port.
9) Gibralter.
10) Sailing of the Glory.

Group 3. Special authors.

(a) Masefield
* 1) Sea Fever
* 2) Christmas, 1903
* 3) West Wind
* 4) Cargoes

(b) Thomas Harding
1) Darkling thrush *
2) Shelley's skylark *
(c) V. Sackville West
1) Mirage *
2) Nomads.
3) Saxon song

① L. Binyon
① "for the fallen *
2. Holiday
3. Thistle *

𝔈𝔫𝔤𝔩𝔦𝔰𝔥 𝔏𝔦𝔱𝔢𝔯𝔞𝔱𝔲𝔯𝔢 𝔖𝔢𝔯𝔦𝔢𝔰.   No. 61.

General Editor:—J. H. FOWLER, M.A.

A SECOND BOOK OF MODERN POETRY

MACMILLAN AND CO., Limited
LONDON · BOMBAY · CALCUTTA · MADRAS
MELBOURNE

THE MACMILLAN COMPANY
NEW YORK · BOSTON · CHICAGO
DALLAS · ATLANTA · SAN FRANCISCO

THE MACMILLAN COMPANY
OF CANADA, LIMITED
TORONTO

A Second Book of Modern Poetry

Selected and Arranged by

H. A. Treble, M.A.

MACMILLAN AND CO., LIMITED
ST. MARTIN'S STREET, LONDON
1932

PRINTED IN GREAT BRITAIN

CONTENTS

NOTE OF ACKNOWLEDGMENT

FOR permission to use copyright poems, the Editor desires to express his sincere thanks to the following authors and publishers : Mr. Martin Armstrong, for " The Thrush," from *The Buzzards* (Martin Secker) ; Mr. J. Redwood Anderson, for " The Bridge," from *Walls and Hedges* (Messrs. Sidgwick & Jackson, Ltd.) ; Messrs. Edward Arnold & Co., for " Thobal," from *The Violet Crown* by Sir Rennell Rodd ; Mr. Laurence Binyon, for " Holiday," " The Thistle," and (with the permission of the Editor of *The Times*) " For the Fallen " ; Mr. Basil Blackwell, for " Essex " by A. S. Cripps ; Mr. G. F. Bradby, for " Marsh Marigolds " and " To a Thrush," from *Broadland* (Elkin Mathews, Ltd.) ; Dr. Robert Bridges, for " Spring Goeth all in White " ; Mr. Charles Dalmon, for " The Ancient Faith " reprinted from *A Poor Man's Riches*, by permission of the author and Messrs. Methuen & Co., Ltd. ; Mr. Walter de la Mare, for " Nod " ; Messrs. Duckworth & Co., for " He does not Die," from *Verses* by Mr. Hilaire Belloc ; Mr. Wilfrid Wilson Gibson and Elkin Mathews, Ltd., for " Flannan Isle " ; Mr. Thomas Hardy, for " Shelley's Skylark " and " The Darkling Thrush " ; Mrs. Katharine Tynan Hinkson, for " Pink Almond " ; Mr. Ralph Hodgson, for " Time, you old Gipsy Man," and " The Bull " ; Mr. Bernard Holland and Messrs. Longmans, Green & Co., for " I vow to thee, my Country," by Sir Cecil Spring-Rice ; Mr. John Lane, the Bodley Head, Ltd., for " In Romney Marsh " and " A Cinque Port," from *Ballads and Songs* by John Davidson, and for " Nomads," from *Poems of East and West*, and " Mirage " and " A Saxon Song," from *Orchard and Vineyard*, by Miss V. Sackville-West ; Messrs. Erskine MacDonald, Ltd., for " The Song of the Fixture Card," from *Sunrise Dreams* by Lieutenant Eric Wilkinson ; Mr. John Masefield, for " Christmas, 1903," " Sea Fever," " The West Wind," and " Cargoes " ; Mr. E. Hamilton Moore, for " Pan," from *The Fountain of Ablutions* (Messrs. W. Heffer & Sons, Ltd.) ; Sir Henry Newbolt, for " San Stefano," from *Poems New and Old* (Mr. John Murray) ; Mr. Alfred Noyes, for " The Dream-Child's Invitation," from the author's *Collected Poems* (Messrs. W. Blackwood & Son) ; Mr. Will H. Ogilvie, for " A Leaf on the Water " ; Messrs. Grant Richards, Ltd., for " Lullaby," from *The Sea is Kind* by Mr. T. Sturge Moore ; Messrs. Selwyn and Blount, Ltd., for " The Sailing of the *Glory*," from *Fifty Poems*, and " Happy is England Now," from *Stone Trees*, by Mr. John Freeman ; Messrs. Sidgwick & Jackson, Ltd., for " The Hunter," from *The Hunter* by Mr. W. J. Turner ; Dr. W. R. Sorley for " The Song of the Ungirt Runners," by Captain C. H. Sorley ; Mr. J. C. Squire and Messrs. Hodder & Stoughton, Ltd., for " Sonnet," from *Poems, First Series* ; Mr. James Stephens, for " The Snare," from *Songs from the Clay* ; Mrs. A. F. Trotter, for " Picardie," from *Nigel and Other Poems* (Messrs. Burns, Oates and Washbourne, Ltd.) ; Mrs. Margaret L. Woods and Mr. John Murray for "The Ballad of King Hjörward's Death" and "The Mariners"; and Mr. W. B. Yeats and Messrs. T. Fisher Unwin, Ltd., for "The Lake Isle of Innisfree."

Moreover, the Editor is especially grateful for much advice and assistance to the General Editor of the series in which this little collection of Modern Poems appears, and to his colleague, Mr. G. H. Vallins, for generous aid in the preparation and testing of the exercises.

CROYDON,
   October, 1923.

FLANNAN ISLE

" THOUGH three men dwell on Flannan Isle
　To keep the lamp alight,
　As we steer'd under the lee, we caught
　No glimmer through the night."

A passing ship at dawn had brought
　The news ; and quickly we set sail,
　To find out what strange thing might ail
　The keepers of the deep-sea light.

The winter day broke blue and bright,
　With glancing sun and glancing spray,　　　10
　As o'er the swell our boat made way,
　As gallant as a gull in flight.

But, as we near'd the lonely Isle ;
　And look'd up at the naked height ;
　And saw the lighthouse towering white,
With blinded lantern, that all night
　Had never shot a spark
　Of comfort through the dark,
So ghostly in the cold sunlight
It seem'd, that we were struck the while　　　20
With wonder all too dread for words.

And, as into the tiny creek
　We stole beneath the hanging crag,
　We saw three queer, black, ugly birds—

Too big, by far, in my belief,
For guillemot or shag [1]—
Like seamen sitting bolt-upright
Upon a half-tide reef :
But, as we near'd, they plunged from sight,
Without a sound, or spurt of white.   30

And still too 'mazed to speak,
We landed ; and made fast the boat ;
And climb'd the track in single file,
Each wishing he was safe afloat,
On any sea, however far,
So it be far from Flannan Isle :
And still we seem'd to climb, and climb,
As though we'd lost all count of time,
And so must climb for evermore.
Yet, all too soon, we reached the door—   40
The black, sun-blister'd lighthouse-door,
That gaped for us ajar.

As, on the threshold, for a spell,
We paused, we seem'd to breathe the smell
Of limewash and of tar,
Familiar as our daily breath,
As though 'twere some strange scent of death :
And so, yet wondering, side by side,
We stood a moment, still tongue-tied :
And each with black foreboding eyed   50
The door, ere we should fling it wide,
To leave the sunlight for the gloom :
Till, plucking courage up, at last,
Hard on each other's heels we pass'd
Into the living-room.

Yet, as we crowded through the door,
We only saw a table, spread

[1] The crested cormorant.

For dinner, meat and cheese and bread ;
But all untouch'd ;   and no one there :
As though, when they sat down to eat,   60
Ere they could even taste,
Alarm had come ; and they in haste
Had risen and left the bread and meat :
For at the table-head a chair
Lay tumbled on the floor.

We listen'd ; but we only heard
The feeble cheeping of a bird
That starved upon its perch :
And, listening still, without a word,
We set about our hopeless search.   70
We hunted high, we hunted low ;
And soon ransack'd the empty house ;
Then o'er the Island, to and fro,
We ranged, to listen and to look
In every cranny, cleft or nook
That might have hid a bird or mouse :
But, though we search'd from shore to shore,
We found no sign in any place :
And soon again stood face to face
Before the gaping door :   80
And stole into the room once more
As frighten'd children steal.

Aye : though we hunted high and low,
And hunted everywhere,
Of the three men's fate we found no trace
Of any kind in any place,
But a door ajar, and an untouch'd meal,
And an overtoppled chair.

And, as we listen'd in the gloom
Of that forsaken living-room—   90

A chill clutch on our breath—
We thought how ill-chance came to all
Who kept the Flannan Light :
And how the rock had been the death
Of many a likely lad :
How six had come to a sudden end,
And three had gone stark mad :
And one whom we'd all known as friend
Had leapt from the lantern one still night,
And fallen dead by the lighthouse wall :   100
And long we thought
On the three we sought,
And of what might yet befall.

Like curs, a glance has brought to heel,
We listen'd, flinching there :
And look'd, and look'd, on the untouch'd meal,
And the overtoppled chair.

We seem'd to stand for an endless while,
Though still no word was said,
Three men alive on Flannan Isle,   110
Who thought on three men dead.

                        WILFRID WILSON GIBSON.

2.   THE BALLAD OF KING HJÖRWARD'S DEATH

THE Norns decreed in their high home,
   "Hjörward the King must die to-day,"—
A mighty man, but old and gray
With housing long on the gray foam,
And driving on their perilous way
His hungry dragon-herd to seek
Their fiery pastures, and to wreak

On Southern shrines with flame and sword
The wrath of Asgard's dreadful lord.

Seven days King Hjörward then had kept   10
His place in silence on his throne,
Seven nights had left him there alone,
Watching while all the palace slept,
Wan in the dawn and still as stone.
But when they said, " The King must die,"
A shout such as in days gone by
Shook the good ship when swords were swung,
Broke from his heart and forth he sprung.

" Sword, sword and shield ! " he cried, " and thou
Haste, let the winged ship fly free.   20
Yonder there shivers the pale sea,
Impatient for the plunging prow,
I hear the shrill wind call to me—
Hark, how it hastens from the east !
' Why tarriest thou ? ' it cries, ' the feast
To-night in Odin's hall is spread,
They wait thee there, the armed dead.'

" They wait me there ! Ho, sword and shield !
What hero-faces throng the gate !
Not long nor vainly shall ye wait.   30
I too have not been weak to wield
The heavy brand, I too am great,
Hjörward am I.   No funeral car
Slow rolling, but a ship of war
Swift on the wind and racing wave,
Bears me to feast among the brave.

" Slaves, women, shall not sail with me,
Nor broidered stuffs, nor hoarded gold,
But men, my liegemen from of old,

Strong men to ride the unbroken sea,   40
And arms such as befit the bold.
Come forth, my steed, thou fierce and fleet,
Once more thy flying hoofs shall beat
The level way along the strand,
The hard bright sea-forsaken sand."

So the horse Halfi came, and rose
The hounds that wont to hunt with him,
Shaggy of hide and lithe of limb.
And we too followed where repose
The dragon-ships in order grim,   50
Hastening together to let slip
Svior, the dark shield-girdled ship,
That like a live thing from the steep
Fled eagerly into the deep.

Fly fast to-day—proud ship, fly fast,
Scatter the surge and drink the spray ;
Hjörward is at thy helm to-day
For the last time, and for the last
Last time thou treadst the windy way.
The oarsmen to the chiming oar   60
Chant their hoarse song, and on the shore
The folk are silent watching thee
Speeding across the wide cold sea.

The wind that rose with day's decline
Rent the dim curtain of the west ;
Clear o'er the water's furthest crest
We saw a sudden splendour shine,
A flying flame that smote the breast
And high head of the mailed King,
His hoary beard and glittering   70
Great brand in famous fights renowned,
And those grim chiefs that girt him round.

" The gate," he muttered, " lo ! the gate ! "
Staring upon the sky's far gold.
Yea, the wild clouds about it rolled
Showed like the throned and awful state
Of gods whose feet the waves enfold,
Whose brows the voyaging tempests smite,
Who wait, assembled at the bright
Valhalla doors, the sail that brings   80
This last and mightiest of kings.

As swift before the wind we drave,
We surely heard from far within
Their shining battlements the din
Of that proud sword-play of the brave ;
And Hjörward cried, " The games begin,
The clang of shield on shield I hear.
Wait, sons of Odin, wait your peer ! "
Then as that sudden splendour fled,
With one great shout the King fell dead.   90

Lo as some falcon struck in flight
Reels from her course, and dizzily
Beats with loose pinions down the sky,
So Svior reeled 'twixt height and height
Of mounting waves, and heavily
Plunged in the black trough of the sea ;
And o'er her helmless, full of glee,
The roaring waters leapt and fell,
Sweeping swift souls of men to Hell.

We seized the helm and lowered the mast,   100
And shorewards steered thro' night and wind ;
We seemed like loiterers left behind
By some bright pageant that had passed
Within and left to us the blind
Shut gates and twilight ways forlorn.
And coldly rose the strange new morn,

Ere to the watchers on the shore
We cried, " The King returns no more."

Return, ah ! once again return !
Cross the frail bridge at close of day,   110
And pale along the crimson way
Of sunset when the first stars burn,
Ride forth, thou king-born—look and say
If on the wide earth stretched beneath
Thou seest any house of death,
High sepulchre where monarchs be,
Like thine up-built beside the sea.

Far have I journeyed from the moan
Of Northern waters, wandering
By tombs of many a famous king,   120
Where swathed in shrouds and sealed in stone
They slumber, and the tapers fling
A dimness o'er them, and the drone
Of praying priests they hear alone ;
Shut out from earth and bounteous sky
And all the royal life gone by.

But Hjörward, clothed in shining mail,
Holds kingly state even where he died,
At Svior's helm.   On either side
The hoary chiefs who loved to sail   130
In youth with him sit full of pride,
Leaned on their arms and painted shields,
Dim from a thousand battle-fields,
Looking upon the King, and he
Turns his helmed brows towards the sea.

Across his knees his naked brand
Is laid, and underneath his feet
The Goth horse Halfi, and the fleet
Great hounds he loved beneath his hand,

And when the storms arise there beat   140
Salt surges up against his grave.
He surely sometimes feels the brave
Ship Svior quiver in her sleep,
Dreaming she treads the windy deep.

There overhead year after year
The moorland turf and thyme shall grow,
Above the horizon faint and low
The same wild mountain summits peer ;
The same gray gleamy sea shall sow
With foam the level leagues of sand,   150
And peace be with that warrior band,
Till dim below the bright abodes
Gather the twilight of the gods.

                                    MARGARET L. WOODS.

3.   THOBAL

(*Relating to an episode in the outbreak in Manipur*, 1892, *when
Lieutenant Grant held the little fort of Thobal against tremendous
odds and won the V.C.*)

THERE was deadly work in the border hills, as it drew to
        Easter-tide,
And the flag that waved for England was humbled there in
        its pride.

They were grim familiar tidings, those few dark words of
        doom,
For the wide outposts of Empire are marked by the lonely
        tomb ;—

There was no new phase in the story, but another page writ
        red,
The ambush laid, and the few too few, and the roll of English
        dead !

And we doubted not of the duty done, we were sure they had
    died like men,
And we knew that the flag of England would float on its mast
    again.

But it chanced there were thirty Ghoorkas who were marching
    on their way,
With fifty more of the Burman folk that have learned the
    word " obey,"   10

When the scouts brought in the tidings, and the blood lust
    made them mad,
These eighty men of the loyal folk led on by an English lad.

And he did not wait nor waver, he took no count of the odds,
For he knew that he stood for England in the face of the
    painted gods ;

Though the hills poured down their thousands, if the sturdy
    pluck held true,
He would stand his ground and show them what an English
    lad could do.

So a week went by in silence, and at last the message came,
And the eighty men of Thobal had saved the English name.

Then speak, oh mother island, for was it not well done ?
Be proud of thy step-children, and proudest of thy son !   20

Once more the world has seen it, far under alien skies,
The beating heart of England is where the old flag flies.

What though they deem thou sleepest, and smile to see thee
    range,
And follow wandering voices on many a wind of change ;

What though men say thy gospel is the counter and the till,
The boys we send to the far world's end have the heart of the
    lion still—

The heart of Richard Grenville when he fought with the
    fifty-three,
As he bled to death in the battered hull that was lost in the
    Spanish sea ;

The heart of Walter Raleigh, and the heart of Francis Drake,
The heart of all the heroes who have lived for England's sake; 30

The heart of those who ventured on many a hopeless quest,
Till their dear divine unreason had joined the east and west.

You boys that man the warships that are the ocean queen's,
Come back and tell your fathers what that name of England
    means.

Round all the world's wide girdle, in Asia's dark defiles,
In the yellow sands of torrid lands, in tempest-sundered isles,

O'er many a lonely station the trebled crosses wave,
For justice to the weaker, and for freedom to the slave !

God send her rulers wisdom,—the task to tame the lands,
The peril path of Empire is safe in these young hands.   40

Though the air be filled with strange new sound, and perplexed
    with doubtful creeds,
The boys we send to the far world's end still know what
    England needs.

                        RENNELL RODD.

4.   THE SONG OF THE FIXTURE CARD

(*Written on receipt of the Football Match List from Ilkley
Grammar School*)

    You came by last night's mail
        To my strange little mud-built house,
    At a time when the blues were on my trail
        And I'd little to do but grouse.

For the world seemed a-swim with ooze,
  With everything going wrong,
And though I knew that we couldn't lose,
  Yet the end of it all seemed long.
The sandbag bed felt hard,
  And exceedingly cold the rain,   10
But you sang to me, little green card,
  And gave me courage again ;
For at sight of the old green back
  And the dear familiar crest,
I was off and away on memory's track,
Where Rumbold's Moor stands bleak and black
  And the plaintive curlews nest.
Then, thin and clear, I seemed to hear—
  Now low and sweet, now high and strong—
A note of cheer to banish fear ;   20
  The little card sang thus his song.

The Song

There's a broad green field in a broad green vale,
  There's a bounding ball and a straining pack ;
There's a clean cold wind blowing half a gale,
  There's a strong defence and a swift attack.
There's a roar from the " touch " like an angry sea,
  As the struggle wavers from goal to goal ;
But the fight is clean as a fight should be,
  And they're friends when the ball has ceased to roll.
Clean and keen is the grand old rule,   30
  And heart and courage must never fail.
They are making men where the grey stone school
  Looks out on the broad green vale.
    Can you hear the call ?   Can you hear the call ?
    Now, School ! Now, School ! Play up !
There's many a knock and many a fall
For those who follow a Rugger ball ;

But hark !—can you hear it ? Over all—
    Now, School ! Now, School ! Play up !

She makes her men and she sends them forth,   40
    O proud old mother of many sons !
The Ilkley breed has proved its worth
    Wherever the bond of Empire runs ;
But near or far the summons clear
    Has sought them out from town and heath,
They've met the foeman with a cheer,
    And face to face have smiled on death.
They are fighting still to the grand old rule,
    That heart and courage must never fail—
If they fall, there are more where the grey stone school
    Looks out on the broad green vale.   51
      Can you hear the call ? Can you hear the call
      That drowns the roar of Krupp ?
There are many who fight and many who fall
Where the big guns play at the Kaiser's ball,
But hark !—can you hear it ?   Over all—
    Now, School ! Now, School ! Play up !

So when old age has won the fight
    That godlike youth can never win,
The mind turns from the coming night,   60
    To boyish visions flooding in ;
And by the hearth the old man dreams
    Of school and all it meant to him,
Till in the firelight's kindly beams
    The wise old eyes grow very dim.
But he's lived his life to the grand old rule
    That heart and courage must never fail ;
So he lifts his glass to the grey stone school
    That looks on the broad green vale.
      Can you hear the call ? Can you hear the call ? 70
      Here's a toast, now ! Fill the cup !

Though the shadow of fate is on the wall,
Here's a final toast ere the darkness fall—
" The days of our boyhood—best of all ! "
    Now, School ! Now, School ! Play up !

ERIC WILKINSON.

5.   THE SONG OF THE UNGIRT RUNNERS

WE swing ungirded hips,
And lightened are our eyes,
The rain is on our lips,
We do not run for prize.
We know not whom we trust
Nor whitherward we fare,
But we run because we must
    Through the great wide air.

The waters of the seas
Are troubled as by storm.   10
The tempest strips the trees
And does not leave them warm.
Does the tearing tempest pause ?
Do the tree-tops ask it why ?
So we run without a cause
    'Neath the big bare sky.

The rain is on our lips,
We do not run for prize.
But the storm the water whips
And the wave howls to the skies.   20
The winds arise and strike it
And scatter it like sand,
And we run because we like it
    Through the broad bright land.

C. H. SORLEY.

6.   SAN STEFANO

                (*A Ballad of the Bold* Menelaus)

IT was morning at St. Helen's, in the great and gallant days,
  And the sea beneath the sun glittered wide,
When the frigate set her courses, all a-shimmer in the haze,
  And she hauled her cable home and took the tide.
She'd a right fighting company, three hundred men and more,
  Nine and forty guns in tackle running free ;
And they cheered her from the shore for her colours at the fore,
  When the bold *Menelaus* put to sea.

She'd a right fighting company, three hundred men and more,
  Nine and forty guns in tackle running free ;   10
And they cheered her from the shore for her colours at the fore,
  When the bold Menelaus *put to sea.*

She was clear of Monte Cristo, she was heading for the land,
  When she spied a pennant red and white and blue ;
They were foemen, and they knew it, and they'd half a league
      in hand,
  But she flung aloft her royals and she flew.
She was nearer, nearer, nearer, they were caught beyond a
      doubt,
  But they slipped her, into Orbetello Bay,
And the lubbers gave a shout as they paid their cables out,
  With the guns grinning round them where they lay.   20

Now Sir Peter was a captain of a famous fighting race,
  Son and grandson of an admiral was he ;
And he looked upon the batteries, he looked upon the chase,
  And he heard the shout that echoed out to sea.

And he called across the decks, " Ay ! the cheering might be
    late
    If they kept it till the *Menelaus* runs ;
Bid the master and his mate heave the lead and lay her
    straight
    For the prize lying yonder by the guns."

When the summer moon was setting, into Orbetello Bay
    Came the *Menelaus* gliding like a ghost ;   30
And her boats were manned in silence, and in silence pulled
    away,
    And in silence every gunner took his post.
With a volley from her broadside the citadel she woke,
    And they hammered back like heroes all the night ;
But before the morning broke she had vanished through the
    smoke
    With her prize upon her quarter grappled tight.

It was evening at St. Helen's, in the great and gallant time,
    And the sky behind the down was flushing far ;
And the flags were all a-flutter, and the bells were all a-chime,
    When the frigate cast her anchor off the bar.   40
She'd a right fighting company, three hundred men and more,
    Nine and forty guns in tackle running free ;
And they cheered her from the shore for her colours at the
    fore,
    When the bold *Menelaus* came from sea.

She'd a right fighting company, three hundred men and more,
    Nine and forty guns in tackle running free ;
And they cheered her from the shore for her colours at the fore,
    When the bold Menelaus *came from sea.*

                   HENRY NEWBOLT.

*colour —
fig. speech ×   ×
use of ~sounds~*

7.   CHRISTMAS, 1903

O, THE sea breeze will be steady, and the tall ship's going trim,
And the dark blue skies are paling, and the white stars
    burning dim ;
The long night watch is over, and the long sea-roving done,
And yonder light is the Start Point light, and yonder comes
    the sun.

O, we have been with the Spaniards, and far and long on the sea;
But there are the twisted chimneys, and the gnarled old inns
    on the quay.
The wind blows keen as the day breaks, the roofs are white
    with the rime,
And the church-bells ring as the sun comes up to call men in
    to Prime.

The church-bells rock and jangle, and there is peace on the
    earth,
Peace and good-will and plenty and Christmas games and
    mirth.   10
O, the gold glints bright on the wind-vane as it shifts above
    the squire's house,
And the water of the bar of Salcombe is muttering about the
    bows.

O, the salt sea tide of Salcombe, it wrinkles into wisps of
    foam,
And the church-bells ring in Salcombe to ring poor sailors
    home.
The belfry rocks as the bells ring, the chimes are merry as a
    song,
They ring home wandering sailors who have been homeless
    long.

                                        JOHN MASEFIELD.

long, broad, sweeping

8.   SEA FEVER

I MUST down to the seas again, to the lonely sea and the
    sky,
And all I ask is a tall ship and a star to steer her by ;
And the wheel's kick and the wind's song and the white
    sail's shaking,
And a grey mist on the sea's face and a grey dawn breaking.

I must down to the seas again, for the call of the running
    tide
Is a wild call and a clear call that may not be denied ;
And all I ask is a windy day with the white clouds flying,
And the flung spray and the blown spume, and the sea-gulls
    crying.

I must down to the seas again, to the vagrant gypsy life,
To the gull's way and the whale's way where the wind's like
    a whetted knife ;   10
And all I ask is a merry yarn from a laughing fellow-rover,
And quiet sleep and a sweet dream when the long trick's over.

                                        JOHN MASEFIELD.

9.   NOMADS

FROM the shores of the Atlantic to the gardens of Japan,
From the darkness of the Neva to the courts of Ispahan,
There is nothing that can hold us, hold our wandering caravan.

Leisurely is our encamping ; nowhere pause in hasty flight.
Long enough to learn the secret, and the value, and the might,
Whether of the northern mountains or the southern lands of
    light.

And the riches of the regions will be ours from land to land,
Falling as a willing booty under our marauding hand,
Rugs from Persia, gods from China, emeralds from Samarcand!

And the old forgotten empires, which have faded turn by
    turn,   10
From the shades emerging slowly to their ancient sway return,
And to their imperial manhood rise the ashes from the urn.

We have known Byzantium's glory when the eagled flag was
    flown,
When the ruins were not ruins ; eagled visions have I known
Of a spectral Roman emperor seated on a spectral throne.

We have tasted space and freedom, frontiers falling as we went,
Now with narrow bonds and limits never could we be content,
For we have abolished boundaries, straightened borders have
    we rent,
And a house no more confines us than the roving nomad's
    tent.

                    V. SACKVILLE-WEST
          (THE HON. MRS. HAROLD NICOLSON).

10.   MIRAGE

THERE travelled north from Kurdistan along the lone Siberian
    trails
A merchant with his caravan and Eastern barter in his bales.
He rode ahead, he rode apart, the city of Irkutsk his goal,
Upon his lean Circassian foal, and after came the lumbering
    cart
With creaking wheel, deliberate spoke, and water-bullocks in
    the yoke ;
And after these in single string the boorish camels following,

Slouching with high unwieldy packs like howdahs piled upon
    their backs ;

With slaver hanging from their lips and hatred worming in
    their brain

They slouched beneath their drivers' whips across the white
    and mournful plain.

The merchant riding on alone saw not the white incessant
    snow,   10

He only saw the metal's glow, the colour of the precious stone ;

He lingered on the merchandise that he had brought from
    Kurdistan,

And turned, and swept his caravan with doting and voluptuous
    eyes,

For there were choice Bokhara rugs, and daggers with
    Damascus blade

And hafts of turquoise-studded jade, and phials rich with
    scented drugs,

Koràns inscribed on ass's skin, and bales of silk from Temesvàr,

And silver ear-rings beaten thin, and bargains from the cool
    bazaar.

He felt the gold already pouched, he crooned to it with horrid
    love,

As still the camels onward slouched with hatred of the men
    that drove.

For thirty days the caravan trailed on behind the merchant's
    foal,   20

Through Persia and through Turkestan, the city of Irkutsk
    their goal ;

They passed the fruitful hill-girt lands where dwelt the fair-
    skinned Grecian race,

And came into the wilder place, and sighted vagrant Cossack
    bands

That wandered with their flocks and herds, and trafficked
    with the train of Kurds ;

They stirred the ghost of Tamerlane, who swept that way with
    Tartar hordes,
The ghosts of dead barbarian lords, the Asiatic hurricane ;
They crossed the mighty road that runs from Moscow through
    to China's wall,
And trod the path of nomad Huns and knew Siberia's white
    pall
When fields of Persian asphodel were visions of a distant day
And boundless snow around them lay, and noiseless snow for
    ever fell,   30
Where soon the fleeting day was done, and on the hard
    horizon low
They saw the scarlet ball of sun divided by the ridge of
    snow
Sink down in skies incarnadine ; and still with their disjointed
    gait
And nursing their malignant hate, the camels kept unbroken
    line.

When yet a hundred miles or more stretched out between
    them and their goal
The merchant riding on before drew rein on his Circassian foal
And called a halt with lifted hand as he had done unfailingly
Each night since the monotony began with that unvaried land.
The dusk was suddenly alive as shouting voices passed the
    word,
And all the drowsy train was stirred with movement like a
    shaken hive.   40
The master merchant stiff from cramp was calling for his
    saddle flask,
As each to his accustomed task ran swiftly in the growing
    camp.
A tent like an inverted bell, all scarlet with the dyes of Tyre,
Was lifted rapidly and well, and like a torch the kindled fire
Destroyed the night with leaping tongue, and in a circle round
    the glow

Men shovelled back the melting snow, and skins and Khelim
    rugs were flung—
And unforgotten were the needs of water-bullocks standing by
Whose brows are stained with orange dye, whose horns are
    looped with turquoise beads.
The pariah dogs that slink and prowl secured their meat with
    furtive growl,
And one by one the camels bent complaining to their warty
    knees   50
And grumbled at the men that went to loose their girths and
    give them ease.

The merchant brooded silently on avaricious visions bright
And listened to the revelry his men were making in the night.
For one, a young and favourite Kurd, a mongrel child of the
    bazaar,
Whose voice was like a singing bird, was striking on a harsh
    guitar—

> I know a Room where tulips tall
>   And almond-blossom pale
> Are coloured on the frescoed wall.
>
> I know a River where the ships
>   Drift by with ghostly sail   60
> And dead men chant with merry lips.
>
> I know the Garden by the sea
>   Where birds with painted wings
> Mottle the dark magnolia Tree.
>
> I know the never-failing Source,
>   I know the Bush that sings,
> The Vale of Gems, the flying Horse.
>
> I know the Dog that was a Prince,
>   The talking Nightingale,
> The Hill of Glass, the magic Quince.   70

I know the lovely Lake of Van ;
Yet, knowing all these things,
I wander with a Caravan,
I wander with a Caravan !

The cold moon rose remotely higher, insensibly the voices
    hushed,
And men with wine and laughter flushed were sleeping all
    around the fire,
Till one alone sat on erect, his ready gun across his knees,
The sentry of the night elect, guardian of sleeping destinies.
The water-bullocks lay as dead ; the dogs drew near with
    noiseless tread,
And huddled in a loose-limbed heap beside the fire, and
    through their sleep   80
They twitched at some remembered hunt ; the merchant in
    his sheepskin rolled
Within the tent saw dreams of gold ; the camels with uneasy
    grunt
And quake of their distorted backs slept on with loathing by
    their packs.

At dawn the weary sentry rose to throw some brushwood
    on the flames,
Called on his comrades by their names, and turned to greet
    the endless snows,
But then from his astonished lips a cry of unbelieving
    rang
And all the men towards him sprang, the camel drivers with
    their whips,
The bullock driver with his yoke, and gazed in loud bewilder-
    ment
Till slowly in his fur-lined cloak the merchant issued from his
    tent.
Then he too started at the sight and clamoured with his
    clamorous men,   90

And swore he could not see aright, and rubbed his eyes and
    stared again ;

The camels came with lurching tread and stood in loose
    fantastic ring

With necks outstretched and swaying head and mouths all
    slackly slobbering,

And drew from some unclean recess within their body's
    secret lair

A bladder smeared with filthiness that bubbled on the morning
    air.

For there upon the shining plain a city radiantly lay,

All coloured in the rising day, amid the snow a jewelled
    stain,

And in her walls a spacious gate gave entrance to a varied
    stream

Of folk that went incorporate like figures in a silent dream,

And high above the roofs arose, more coloured for the hueless
    snows,   100

The domes of churches, bronze and green, like peacocks in their
    painted sheen.

The merchant, with a trembling hand extended far, extended
    wide

Against illusion's fairyland, at length articulately cried :

" Irkutsk ! but twice a hundred miles remained of weary
    pilgrimage

Before we hoped with happy smiles to reach our final anchor-
    age.

But look again. That rosy tower that rises like a tulip
    straight

Within the walls beside the gate, a balanced plume, a springing
    flower,

And pointed with a lance-like spire of bronze, was fifty years
    ago

—A boy, I saw it standing so,—demolished and destroyed
    by fire."

And one, a venerable Kurd, took up again the fallen word : 110
" I travelled both as boy and man between Irkutsk and
      Kurdistan,
But never since my beard was grown saw I that inn beside
      the way
Wherewith the Council made away, full fifty counted years
      aflown."

They gazed upon the marvel long, the spectre city wonderful,
Until the youth who made the song cried out, " We grow too
      fanciful.
Irkutsk with roofs of coloured tiles lies distant twice a hundred
      miles,
And this, a city of the shades, a rainbow of the echoing air,
As fair as false, and false as fair, already into nothing fades."

And like a bubble, like the mist that in the valley faintly
      swirls,
Like orient sheen on sulky pearls, like hills remotely
      amethyst,   120
Like colours on Phœnician glass, like plumage on the 'fisher's
      wing,
Like music on the breath of spring, they saw the vision lift
      and pass,
Till only white unbroken snow stretched out before the
      caravan,
And the bewildered heart of man truth from delusion could
      not know.
But all the long laborious train moved slowly on its course
      again
Across the snow unbroken, white, and nursing each his private
      creed,
The merchant his illusive greed, the camels their illusive spite.

                                        V. SACKVILLE-WEST.

11.   THE MARINERS

THE mariners sleep by the sea.
The wild wind comes up from the sea,
It wails round the tower, and it blows through the grasses,
It scatters the sand o'er the graves where it passes
And the sound and the scent of the sea.

The white waves beat up from the shore,
They beat on the church by the shore,
They rush round the grave-stones aslant to the leeward,
And the wall and the mariners' graves lying seaward,
That are bank'd with the stones from the shore.   10

For the huge sea comes up in the storm,
Like a beast from the lair of the storm,
To claim with its ravenous leap and to mingle
The mariners' bones with the surf and the shingle
That it rolls round the shore in the storm.

There is nothing beyond but the sky,
But the sea and the slow-moving sky,
Where a cloud from the grey lifts the gleam of its edges,
Where the foam flashes white from the shouldering ridges,
As they crowd on the uttermost sky.   20

The mariners sleep by the sea.
Far away there's a shrine by the sea;
The pale women climb up the path to it slowly,
To pray to Our Lady of Storms ere they wholly
Despair of their men from the sea.

The children at play on the sand,
Where once from the shell-broider'd sand
They would watch for the sails coming in from far places,

Are forgetting the ships and forgetting the faces
Lying here, lying hid in the sand.   30

When at night there's a seething of surf,
The grandames look out o'er the surf,
They reckon their dead and their long years of sadness,
And they shake their lean fists at the sea and its madness,
And curse the white fangs of the surf.

But the mariners sleep by the sea.
They hear not the sound of the sea,
Nor the hum from the church where the psalm is uplifted,
Nor the crying of birds that above them are drifted.
The mariners sleep by the sea.

                                        MARGARET L. WOODS.

12.   THE WEST WIND

IT's a warm wind, the west wind, full of birds' cries ;
I never hear the west wind but tears are in my eyes.
For it comes from the west lands, the old brown hills,
And April's in the west wind, and daffodils.

It's a fine land, the west land, for hearts as tired as mine,
Apple orchards blossom there, and the air's like wine.
There is cool green grass there, where men may lie at rest,
And the thrushes are in song there, fluting from the nest.

" Will ye not come home, brother ?   Ye have been long
    away.
It's April, and blossom time, and white is the may :   10
And bright is the sun, brother, and warm is the rain,
Will ye not come home, brother, home to us again ?

" The young corn is green, brother, where the rabbits run ;
It's blue sky, and white clouds, and warm rain and sun.

It's song to a man's soul, brother, fire to a man's brain,
To hear the wild bees and see the merry spring again.

"Larks are singing in the west, brother, above the green wheat,
So will ye not come home, brother, and rest your tired feet ?
I've a balm for bruised hearts, brother, sleep for aching eyes,"
Says the warm wind, the west wind, full of birds' cries.   20

It's the white road westwards is the road I must tread
To the green grass, the cool grass, and rest for heart and head,
To the violets and the warm hearts and the thrushes' song
In the fine land, the west land, the land where I belong.

JOHN MASEFIELD.

13.   HOLIDAY

THROUGH Ebblesborne and Broad-chalke
The narrow river runs,
Dimples with dark November rains
Flashes in April suns.

But give me days of rosy June
And on warm grass to lie
And watch, bright over long green weed,
Quick water wimple by.

Blue swallows, arrowing up and down,
Cool trout that glide and dart,
Lend me their happy bodies   10
For the fancies of my heart.

But you, clear stream, that murmur
One music all day long,
I wish my idle fancy
Sang half so sweet a song.

LAURENCE BINYON.

14.   HE DOES NOT DIE

He does not die that can bequeath
Some influence to the land he knows,
Or dares, persistent, interwreathe
Love permanent with the wild hedgerows ;
    He does not die, but still remains
    Substantiate with his darling plains.

The spring's superb adventure calls
His dust athwart the woods to flame ;
His boundary river's secret falls
Perpetuate and repeat his name.   10
    He rides his loud October sky :
    He does not die.   He does not die.

The beeches know the accustomed head
Which loved them, and a peopled air
Beneath their benediction spread
Comforts the silence everywhere ;
    For native ghosts return and these
    Perfect the mystery in the trees.

So, therefore, though myself be crosst
The shuddering of that dreadful day   20
When friend and fire and home are lost
And even children drawn away—
    The passer-by shall hear me still,
    A boy that sings on Duncton Hill.

                                    HILAIRE BELLOC.

15.   IN ROMNEY MARSH

As I went down to Dymchurch Wall,
    I heard the South sing o'er the land;
I saw the yellow sunlight fall
    On knolls where Norman churches stand.

And ringing shrilly, taut and lithe,
    Within the wind a core of sound,
The wire from Romney town to Hythe
    Alone its airy journey wound.

A veil of purple vapour flowed
    And trailed its fringe along the Straits;   10
The upper air like sapphire glowed;
    And roses filled Heaven's central gates.

Masts in the offing wagged their tops;
    The swinging waves pealed on the shore;
The saffron beach, all diamond drops
    And beads of surge, prolonged the roar.

As I came up from Dymchurch Wall,
    I saw above the Downs' low crest
The crimson brands of sunset fall,
    Flicker and fade from out the west.   20

Night sank: like flakes of silver fire
    The stars in one great shower came down;
Shrill blew the wind; and shrill the wire
    Rang out from Hythe to Romney town.

The darkly shining salt sea drops
    Streamed as the waves clashed on the shore;
The beach, with all its organ stops
    Pealing again, prolonged the roar.

                                   JOHN DAVIDSON.

Short clauses makes it more dramatic.

16. ESSEX

I GO through the fields of blue water
 On the South road of the sea.
High to North the East-Country
 Holds her green fields to me—
For she that I gave over,
 Gives not over me.

Poet at sea
visits his
home places in
his dreams.

Last night I lay at Good Easter
 Under a hedge I knew,
Last night beyond High Easter
 I trod the May-floors blue—   10
Till from the sea the sun came
 Bidding me wake and rue.

Roding (that names eight churches)—
 Banks with the paigles[1] dight—
Chelmer whose mill and willows
 Keep one red tower in sight—
Under the Southern Cross run
 Beside the ship to-night.

Ah ! I may not seek back now,
 Neither be turned nor stayed.   20
Yet should I live, I'd seek her,
 Once that my vows are paid !
And should I die I'd haunt her—
 I being what God made !

England has greater counties—
 Their peace to hers is small.
Low hills, rich fields, calm rivers,
 In Essex seek them all,—
Essex, where I that found them
 Found to lose them all.

          A. S. CRIPPS.

[1] cowslips.

17.   GIBRALTAR

SEVEN weeks of sea, and twice seven days of storm
Upon the huge Atlantic, and once more
We ride into still water and the calm
Of a sweet evening, screen'd by either shore
Of Spain and Barbary.   Our toils are o'er,
Our exile is accomplish'd.   Once again
We look on Europe, mistress as of yore
Of the fair earth and of the hearts of men.
   Ay, this is the famed rock which Hercules
And Goth and Moor bequeath'd us.   At this door   10
England stands sentry.   God ! to hear the shrill
Sweet treble of her fifes upon the breeze,
And at the summons of the rock gun's roar
To see her red coats marching from the hill !

                         WILFRID SCAWEN BLUNT.

18.   A CINQUE PORT

BELOW the down the stranded town
    What may betide forlornly waits,
With memories of smoky skies,
    When Gallic navies crossed the straits ;
When waves with fire and blood grew bright,
And cannon thundered through the night.

With swinging stride the rhythmic tide
    Bore to the harbour barque and sloop ;
Across the bar the ship of war,
    In castled stern and lanterned poop,   10
Came up with conquests on her lee,
The stately mistress of the sea.

Where argosies have wooed the breeze,
  The simple sheep are feeding now ;
And near and far across the bar
  The ploughman whistles at the plough ;
Where once the long waves washed the shore,
Larks from their lowly lodgings soar.

Below the down the stranded town
  Hears far away the rollers beat ;   20
About the wall the seabirds call ;
  The salt wind murmurs through the street ;
Forlorn the sea's forsaken bride
Awaits the end that shall betide.

                                JOHN DAVIDSON.

19.   PAN

ROUND and about the sordid street
With grimy face and dusty feet,
Tattered jacket, ragged vest,
And flaunting paper plume for crest,
Laughing lips and shining eyes
  —Forget-me-nots from paradise—
And upturned nose impertinent,
With all his tawdry world content—
Pan, of his woodland haunts beguiled,
Is come again, a gutter child,   10
That lightly trips on twinkling toes,
And through a comb and paper blows
Fantastic music as he goes.

                    E. HAMILTON MOORE.

20. ## THE ANCIENT FAITH

O NEVER say that Pan is dead,
And every nymph and satyr fled,
Though, in these days of faithless pride,
Men seldom seek the countryside
On simple pilgrimage to find
The magic pipes Pan leaves behind !

I saw a cherry tree in flower,
All radiant from a passing shower ;
Against the deep blue sky it shone,
Most beautiful to look upon :　　　　　　10
And from the midst of that fair tree
A dryad leaned and smiled to me.

No mortal maid was ever seen
So lovely as that cherry queen !
Hers was the face that sometimes looks
From pages of enchanted books
Where loving workmanship portrays
The beautiful of bygone days.

And if you doubt all ancient lore,
And say that satyrs are no more,　　　　　20
There's many a Sussex croft will show
The marks that, even children know,
Are made upon the grassy ground
By faeries dancing round and round.

O never say that Pan is dead !
But listen for his pipes instead ;
And listen, listen till you hear
His merry music ; sweet and clear
It comes to all the faithful who
Still listen as men used to do.　　　　　30

CHARLES DALMON.

21. MARSH MARIGOLDS

(On the River Ant)

SLATEY skies and a whistling wind
  And a grim gray land,
April here, with a sullen mind
  And a frozen hand !
Hardly a bird with the heart to sing,
  Or a bud that dares to pry ;
Only the plovers hovering
On the lonely marsh, with a heavy wing
  And a sad, slow cry.

Suddenly, round the river bend,   10
  On the homeward race,
Comes the smile of a welcome friend
  With a radiant face ;
Sprinkled thick in a shining mass,
  Bright as a summer beam,
Marigolds in the meadow grass
Bid " God speed " to the ships that pass
  On the wandering stream.

Storm or shine it is all the same,
  Warm or cold,   20
Nothing can daunt the steady flame
  Of the marigold.
Glow of the king-cup, gold of the broom,
  They will show when the worst is done ;
But you are here in the April gloom,
And where'er you blaze and where'er you bloom,
  There is always sun.

Marigolds in the meadows there
  That the waters kiss,

Take my welcome and greet you fair,   30
    For you teach me this :
How I might play a manlier part
    Than the life I lead to-day,
If I could only learn the art
Of keeping sunshine still in the heart
    When the world is gray.

G. F. BRADBY.

22.   THE THISTLE

IN a patch of baked earth
At the crumbled cliff's brink,
Where the parching of August
Has cracked a long chink,

Against the blue void
Of still sea and sky
Stands single a thistle,
Tall, tarnished, and dry.

Frayed leaves, spotted brown,
Head hoary and torn,   10
Was ever a weed
Upon earth so forlorn,

So solemnly gazed on
By the sun in his sheen
That prints in long shadow
Its raggedness lean ?

From the sky comes no laughter,
From earth not a moan.
Erect stands the thistle,
Its seeds abroad blown.   20

LAURENCE BINYON.

23.   TO A THRUSH

SING on, brave bird ! through the soft-dropping rain
That dews the listening air,
Sing ever on in that triumphant strain,
Bidding the world prepare,
The cold incredulous world, prepare for Spring,
When scarce a violet shows
Its earliest blossom, like a frightened thing,
Above the melting snows.
No alien voice art thou with alien tongue,
But nurtured here among the storms and showers   10
That speak the ocean's powers,
Comrade of all the seasons, free, and strong,
Singing to English hearts in English song
The music of this island home of ours.

Not thine the perilous quest, when Summer wanes,
Of lands beyond the sea,
Our little England with her trees and lanes
Is world enough for thee,
Enough the gray sweep of our rolling skies,
The low wind on the wold,   20
The murmur of the myriad harmonies
That haunt the field and fold.
Others, returning, sing of southern days,
And far-off landscapes lit with sunnier glow ;
Thou art content to know
The old-world beauty of our woodland ways
That tuned the soul of Shakespeare into praise
By Avon's quiet waters, long ago.

Sing bravely on ! Not all the nightingales
That pipe with tremulous throat   30
Through the long evenings, as the twilight fails,
Can match thy wild sweet note,

The rapturous tones of thy prophetic call
That bids the world rejoice
And fills the barren waste of March with all
The magic of a voice.
Prophet of gladness with the passionate cry,
Kindle our hearts that wither in cold state,
Ere yet it be too late !
Give us thy sense of woods and fields and sky !   40
Oh ! teach us in our grandeur, lest we die,
The love of freedom that alone is great.

                                    G. F. Bradby.

24.   THE THRUSH

From the high rampart of the sleepy town
He watched through twigs of bare and blackened elms
Blue January evening settle down
Out of the sky's serene and watery realms
(Mingling with smoke from every darkened home),
And dull the low red roofs, and permeate
The blurred and winding streets, and urge its gloom
Across the lawns of damp and desolate
Long gardens.   And on all this humble drift
He saw, built up of gloomy atmosphere,   10
The presence of the gray cathedral lift
Its gathered towers.   But very cold and clear
The unfathomed height of sky.   There faintest blues,
Pale violet, paler rose, and ocean-cool
Green beryl gleamed, as strains of many hues
Might meet and swim together in a pool.
But in the westward trees a golden gleam
Deepened and died, and all hung in a dream
        Pure, passionless, and stilled.

Then on a leafless bough the silence thrilled,   20
Took sudden voice, became a soul upspringing

In a pure, untroubled rapture of clear singing :
And the cool furled bud of evening suddenly flowering
Burst to an odorous bloom, and the silver-showering
Fountain-basin of Quietness brimmed over,
And Mortal Life embraced her spirit lover.
But the long former space of evening hush
Sank beyond thought, and that divine unfolding
Became eternity in the heart.

                      O thrush,
On the topmost bough your bill and throat upholding :   30
O small, smooth-feathered body, infinite Voice ;
You pipe from blackening boughs to the faded sky
Not only utterance of your own small joys,
      Child of immensity !

O harp from which the winds draw harmony !
Summer of roses in the seed's small kernel !
You voice the indrawn breath of life, the eternal
Brooding upon itself in ecstasy,
Till time and space are lost in golden weather,
And dead loves rise again and sing together,   40
And the loves unborn with tender life are stirred
      At the summons of a bird.

But he upon the city walls enchanted,
A dark, unmoving shade, forgetful, lone
Among dark tree-trunks, while the bird descanted
Was caught into the song till light was flown.

                           MARTIN ARMSTRONG.

25.   " TIME, YOU OLD GIPSY MAN "

          TIME, you old gipsy man,
            Will you not stay,
          Put up your caravan
            Just for one day ?

All things I'll give you,
Will you be my guest,
Bells for your jennet
Of silver the best,
Goldsmiths shall beat you
A great golden ring,   10
Peacocks shall bow to you,
Little boys sing,
Oh, and sweet girls will
Festoon you with may,
Time, you old gipsy,
Why hasten away ?

Last week in Babylon,
Last night in Rome,
Morning, and in the crush
Under Paul's dome ;   20
Under Paul's dial
You tighten your rein—
Only a moment,
And off once again ;
Off to some city
Now blind in the womb,
Off to another
Ere that's in the tomb.

Time, you old gipsy man,
  Will you not stay,   30
Put up your caravan
  Just for one day ?

                      RALPH HODGSON.

26.   THE LAKE ISLE OF INNISFREE

I WILL arise and go now, and go to Innisfree,
    And a small cabin build there, of clay and wattles made ;
Nine bean rows will I have there, a hive for the honey bee,
    And live alone in the bee-loud glade.

And I shall have some peace there, for peace comes dropping
        slow,
    Dropping from the veils of the morning to where the cricket
        sings ;
There midnight's all a glimmer, and noon a purple glow,
    And evening full of the linnet's wings.

I will arise and go now, for always night and day
    I hear lake water lapping with low sounds by the shore ; 10
While I stand on the roadway, or on the pavements gray,
    I hear it in the deep heart's core.

                                        W. B. YEATS.

27.   THE DREAM-CHILD'S INVITATION

ONCE upon a time !—Ah, now the light is burning dimly,
    Peterkin is here again : he wants another tale !
Don't you hear him whispering—The Wind is in the chimley,
    The ottoman's a treasure-ship, we'll all set sail ?

All set sail ?   No, the wind is very loud to-night :
    The darkness on the waters is much deeper than of yore,
Yet I wonder—hark, he whispers—if the little streets are still
        as bright
    In old Japan, in old Japan, that happy haunted shore.

I wonder—hush, he whispers—if perhaps the world will wake
        again
    When Christmas brings the stories back from where the
        skies are blue,   10

Where clouds are scattering diamonds down on every cottage
    window-pane,
    And every boy's a fairy prince, and every tale is true.

There the sword Excalibur is thrust into the dragon's throat,
    Evil there is evil, black is black, and white is white:
There the child triumphant hurls the villain spluttering into
    the moat;
    There the captured princess only waits the peerless knight.

Fairyland is gleaming there beyond the Sherwood Forest trees,
    There the City of the Clouds has anchored on the plain
All her misty vistas and slumber-rosy palaces
    (*Shall we not, ah, shall we not, wander there again ?*)   20

" Happy ever after " there, the lights of home a welcome fling
    Softly thro' the darkness as the star that shone of old,
Softly over Bethlehem and o'er the little cradled King
    Whom the sages worshipped with their frankincense and gold.

Once upon a time—perhaps a hundred thousand years ago—
    Whisper to me, Peterkin, I have forgotten when !
Once upon a time there was a way, a way we used to know
    For stealing off at twilight from the weary ways of men.

Whisper it, O whisper it—the way, the way is all I need !
    All the heart and will are here and all the deep desire !   30
Once upon a time—ah, now the light is drawing near indeed,
    I see the fairy faces flush to roses round the fire.

Once upon a time—the little lips are on my cheek again,
    Little fairy fingers clasped and clinging draw me nigh,
Dreams, no more than dreams, but they unloose the weary
    prisoner's chain
And lead him from his dungeon ! " What's a thousand years?"
    they cry.

A thousand years, a thousand years, a little drifting dream ago,
  All of us were hunting with a band of merry men,
The skies were blue, the boughs were green, the clouds were
    crisping isles of snow. . .
. . . So Robin blew his bugle, and the Now became the
    Then.   40

ALFRED NOYES.

28.   PINK ALMOND

So delicate, so airy,
  The almond on the tree,
Pink stars that some good fairy
  Has made for you and me.

A little cloud of roses,
  All in a world of gray,
The almond flower uncloses
  Upon the wild March day.

A mist of roses blowing
  The way of fog and sleet,   10
A dust of roses showing
  For gray dust in the street.

Pink snow upon the branches,
  Pink snow-flakes falling down
In rosy avalanches
  Upon the dreary town.

A rain, a shower of roses,
  All in a roseless day
The almond tree uncloses
  Her roses on the gray.   20

KATHARINE TYNAN HINKSON.

29.   " SPRING GOETH ALL IN WHITE "

SPRING goeth all in white,
    Crowned with milk-white may :
In fleecy flocks of light
    O'er heaven the white clouds stray :

White butterflies in the air ;
    White daisies prank the ground :
The cherry and hoary pear
    Scatter their snow around.

                    ROBERT BRIDGES.

30.   A LEAF ON THE WATER

ON the Autumn breeze
    She drifted wide
From the tall elm trees
    To the nut-brown tide ;
I watch her dip
    On its dappled breast,
A golden ship
    On a magic quest.

Under her sail
    Sleeps August's sheen ;
Over her rail
    The May-days lean—
Days when we laughed
    And joys we knew
Before that craft
    Had signed her crew.

Some elf of the elm
    Is surely there,

10

Holding the helm,
  Alert, aware—   20
With puckered frown
  Some woodland fay
Conning her down
  On her seaward way.

When Summer gleamed
  On flower and grass
Who would have dreamed
  That sail would pass ?
In dark December
  When snowflakes fly   30
Who will remember
  That ship went by ?

W. H. OGILVIE.

31.   CARGOES

QUINQUIREME of Nineveh from distant Ophir
Rowing home to haven in sunny Palestine,
With a cargo of ivory,
And apes and peacocks,
Sandalwood, cedarwood, and sweet white wine.

Stately Spanish galleon coming from the Isthmus,
Dipping through the Tropics by the palm-green shores,
With a cargo of diamonds,
Emeralds, amethysts,
Topazes, and cinnamon, and gold moidores.   10

Dirty British coaster with a salt-caked smoke-stack
Butting through the Channel in the mad March days,
With a cargo of Tyne coal,
Road-rails, pig-lead,
Firewood, iron-ware, and cheap tin trays.

JOHN MASEFIELD.

32.　　　　　　　A SAXON SONG

Tools with the comely names,
　　Mattock and scythe and spade,
Couth and bitter as flames,
　　Clean, and bowed in the blade,—
A man and his tools make a man and his trade.

Breadth of the English shires,
　　Hummock [1] and kame [2] and mead,
Tang of the reeking byres,
　　Land of the English breed,—
A man and his land make a man and his creed.　　10

Leisurely flocks and herds,
　　Cool-eyed cattle that come
Mildly to wonted words,
　　Swine that in orchards roam,—
A man and his beasts make a man and his home.

Children sturdy and flaxen
　　Shouting in brotherly strife,
Like the land they are Saxon,
　　Sons of a man and his wife,—
For a man and his loves make a man and his life.　　20

V. SACKVILLE-WEST.

33.　　　　　　　THE BRIDGE

Here, with one leap,
The bridge that spans the cutting ; on its back
The load
Of the main-road,
And under it the railway-track.

---

[1] hillock.　　　　　　[2] ridge of sand and gravel.

Into the plains they sweep,
Into the solitary plains asleep,
The flowing lines, the parallel lines of steel—
Fringed with their narrow grass
Into the plains they pass,   10
The flowing lines, like arms of mute appeal.

A cry
Prolonged across the earth—a call
To the remote horizons and the sky ;
The whole east rushes down them with its light,
And the whole west receives them, with its pall
Of stars and night—
The flowing lines, the parallel lines of steel.

And with the fall
Of darkness, see ! the red   20
Bright anger of the signal, where it flares
Like a huge eye that stares
On some hid danger in the dark ahead.
A twang of wire—unseen
The signal drops ; and now, instead
Of a red eye, a green.

Out of the silence grows
An iron thunder—grows, and roars, and sweeps,
Menacing ! The plain
Suddenly leaps,   30
Startled, from its repose—
Alert and listening.   Now, from the gloom
Of the soft distance, loom
Three lights and, over them, a brush
Of tawny flame and flying spark—
Three pointed lights that rush,
Monstrous, upon the cringing dark.

And nearer, nearer rolls the sound,
Louder the throb and roar of wheels,
The shout of speed, the shriek of steam ;   40
The sloping bank,
Cut into flashing squares, gives back the clank
And grind of metal, while the ground
Shudders and the bridge reels—
As, with a scream,
The train,
A rage of smoke, a laugh of fire,
A lighted anguish of desire,
A dream
Of gold and iron, of sound and flight,   50
Tumultuous roars across the night.

The train roars past—and, with a cry,
Drowned in a flying howl of wind,
Half-stifled in the smoke and blind,
The plain,
Shaken, exultant, unconfined,
Rises, flows on, and follows, and sweeps by,
Shrieking, to lose itself in distance and the sky.

J. REDWOOD ANDERSON.

34.   THE BULL

SEE an old unhappy bull,
Sick in soul and body both,
Slouching in the undergrowth
Of the forest beautiful,
Banished from the herd he led,
Bulls and cows a thousand head.

Cranes and gaudy parrots go
Up and down the burning sky ;
Tree-top cats purr drowsily

In the dim-day green below ;   10
And troops of monkeys, nutting, some,
All disputing, go and come ;

And things abominable sit
Picking offal buck or swine,
On the mess and over it
Burnished flies and beetles shine,
And spiders big as bladders lie
Under hemlocks ten foot high ;

And a dotted serpent curled
Round and round and round a tree,   20
Yellowing its greenery,
Keeps a watch on all the world,
All the world and this old bull
In the forest beautiful.

Bravely by his fall he came :
One he led, a bull of blood
Newly come to lustihood,
Fought and put his prince to shame,
Snuffed and pawed the prostrate head
Tameless even while it bled.   30

There they left him, every one,
Left him there without a lick,
Left him for the birds to pick,
Left him there for carrion,
Vilely from their bosom cast
Wisdom, worth and love at last.

When the lion left his lair
And roared his beauty through the hills,
And the vultures pecked their quills
And flew into the middle air,   40
Then this prince no more to reign
Came to life and lived again.

He snuffed the herd in far retreat,
He saw the blood upon the ground,
And snuffed the burning airs around
Still with beevish odours sweet,
While the blood ran down his head
And his mouth ran slaver red.

Pity him, this fallen chief,
All his splendour, all his strength,   50
All his body's breadth and length
Dwindled down with shame and grief,
Half the bull he was before,
Bones and leather, nothing more.

See him standing dewlap-deep
In the rushes at the lake,
Surly, stupid, half asleep,
Waiting for his heart to break
And the birds to join the flies
Feasting at his bloodshot eyes,—   60

Standing with his head hung down
In a stupor, dreaming things :
Green savannas, jungles brown,
Battlefields and bellowings,
Bulls undone and lions dead
And vultures flapping overhead.

Dreaming things : of days he spent
With his mother gaunt and lean
In the valley warm and green,
Full of baby wonderment,   70
Blinking out of silly eyes
At a hundred mysteries ;

Dreaming over once again
How he wandered with a throng
Of bulls and cows a thousand strong,

Wandered on from plain to plain,
Up the hill and down the dale,
Always at his mother's tail ;

How he lagged behind the herd,
Lagged and tottered, weak of limb, 80
And she turned and ran to him
Blaring at the loathly bird
Stationed always in the skies,
Waiting for the flesh that dies.

Dreaming maybe of a day
When her drained and drying paps
Turned him to the sweets and saps,
Richer fountains by the way,
And she left the bull she bore
And he looked to her no more ; 90

And his little frame grew stout,
And his little legs grew strong,
And the way was not so long ;
And his little horns came out,
And he played at butting trees
And boulder-stones and tortoises,

Joined a game of knobby skulls
With the youngsters of his year,
All the other little bulls,
Learning both to bruise and bear, 100
Learning how to stand a shock
Like a little bull of rock.

Dreaming of a day less dim,
Dreaming of a time less far,
When the faint but certain star
Of destiny burned clear for him,
And a fierce and wild unrest
Broke the quiet of his breast.

And the gristles of his youth
Hardened in his comely pow,   110
And he came to fighting growth,
Beat his bull and won his cow,
And flew his tail and trampled off
Past the tallest, vain enough,

And curved about in splendour full
And curved again and snuffed the airs
As who should say Come out who dares !
And all beheld a bull, a Bull,
And knew that here was surely one
That backed for no bull, fearing none.   120

And the leader of the herd
Looked and saw, and beat the ground,
And shook the forest with his sound,
Bellowed at the loathly bird
Stationed always in the skies,
Waiting for the flesh that dies.

Dreaming, this old bull forlorn,
Surely dreaming of the hour
When he came to sultan power,
And they owned him master-horn,   130
Chiefest bull of all among
Bulls and cows a thousand strong.

And in all the tramping herd
Not a bull that barred his way,
Not a cow that said him nay,
Not a bull or cow that erred
In the furnace of his look
Dared a second, worse rebuke ;

Not in all the forest wide,
Jungle, thicket, pasture, fen,   140
Not another dared him then,

Dared him and again defied ;
Not a sovereign buck or boar
Came a second time for more.

Not a serpent that survived
Once the terrors of his hoof
Risked a second time reproof,
Came a second time and lived,
Not a serpent in its skin
Came again for discipline ;   150

Not a leopard bright as flame,
Flashing fingerhooks of steel
That a wooden tree might feel,
Met his fury once and came
For a second reprimand,
Not a leopard in the land.

Not a lion of them all,
Not a lion of the hills,
Hero of a thousand kills,
Dared a second fight and fall,   160
Dared that ram terrific twice,
Paid a second time the price.

Pity him, this dupe of dream,
Leader of the herd again
Only in his daft old brain,
Once again the bull supreme
And bull enough to bear the part
Only in his tameless heart.

Pity him that he must wake ;
Even now the swarm of flies   170
Blackening his bloodshot eyes
Bursts and blusters round the lake,
Scattered from the feast half-fed
By great shadows overhead ;

And the dreamer turns away
From his visionary herds
And his splendid yesterday,
Turns to meet the loathly birds
Flocking round him from the skies,
Waiting for the flesh that dies.   180

RALPH HODGSON.

35.   LULLABY

LAUGH, laugh,
Laugh gently though,—
For leaves do so,
When the great boughs, to and fro,
Cradle the birds on the tops of the trees, —
Gently they laugh for the love of these.

Sleep, sleep,
Sleep lightly though,—
For birds do so,
Rocked by great boughs to and fro ;
With wind in their feathers, their dreams have wings
And they visit the gardens of numberless kings.

T. STURGE MOORE.

36.   THE HUNTER

BEYOND the blue, the purple seas,
Beyond the thin horizon's line,
Beyond Antilla, Hebrides,
Jamaica, Cuba, Caribbees,
There lies the land of Yucatan.

The land, the land of Yucatan,
The low coast breaking into foam,
The dim hills where my thoughts shall roam
The forests of my boyhood's home,
The splendid dream of Yucatan !　　　　　10

I met thee first long, long ago
Turning a printed page, and I
Stared at a world I did not know
And felt my blood like fire flow
At that strange name of Yucatan.

O those sweet, far-off Austral days
When life had a diviner glow,
When hot Suns whipped my blood to know
Things all unseen, then I could go
Into thy heart, O Yucatan !　　　　　20

I have forgotten what I saw,
I have forgotten what I knew,
And many lands I've set sail for
To find that marvellous spell of yore,
Never to set foot in thy shore,
O haunting land of Yucatan !

But sailing I have passed thee by,
And leaning on the white ship's rail
Watched thy dim hills till mystery
Wrapped thy far stillness close to me　　　　　30
And I have breathed " 'Tis Yucatan !

" 'Tis Yucatan, 'tis Yucatan ! "
The ship is sailing far away
The coast recedes, the dim hills fade,
A bubble-winding track we've made,
And thou'rt a Dream, O Yucatan !

W. J. TURNER.

37.   NOD

SOFTLY along the road of evening,
   In a twilight dim with rose,
Wrinkled with age and drenched with dew,
   Old Nod, the shepherd, goes.

His drowsy flock streams on before him,
   Their fleeces charged with gold,
To where the sun's last beam leans low
   On Nod the shepherd's fold.

The hedge is quick and green with briar,
   From their sand the conies creep ;   10
And all the birds that fly in heaven
   Flock singing home to sleep.

His lambs outnumber a noon's roses,
   Yet, when night's shadows fall,
His blind old sheep-dog, Slumber-soon,
   Misses not one of all.

His are the quiet steeps of dreamland,
   The waters of no-more-pain,
His ram's bell rings 'neath an arch of stars,
   " Rest, rest, and rest again."   20

           WALTER DE LA MARE.

38.   SAILING OF THE *GLORY*

MERRILY shouted all the sailors
   As they left the town behind ;
Merrily shouted they and gladdened
   At the slip-slap of the wind.

[handwritten marginalia:] figurative language / Yet subtlety / in the art yet / the final effect / is one of perfect / simplicity, / and to conceal art,

But envious were those faint home-keepers,
  Faint land-lovers, as they saw
How the *Glory* dipped and staggered—
  Envying saw
Pass the ship while all her sailors
  Merrily shouted.   10

Far and far on eastern waters
  Sailed the ship and yet sailed on,
While the townsmen, faint land-lovers,
  Thought, " How long is't now she's gone ?
Now, maybe, Bombay she touches,
  Now strange craft about her throng " ;
Till she grew but half-remembered,
  Gone so long :
Quite forgot how all her sailors
  Merrily shouted.   20

Far in unfamiliar waters
  Ship and shipmen harbourage found,
Where the rocks creep out like robbers
  After travellers tempest-bound.
Then those faint land-lovers murmured
  Doleful thanks not dead were they :—
Ah, yet envious, though the *Glory*
  Sunken lay,
Hearing again those farewell voices
  Merrily shouting.   30

                              JOHN FREEMAN.

39.   FOR THE FALLEN

WITH proud thanksgiving, a mother for her children,
  England mourns for her dead across the sea.
Flesh of her flesh they were, spirit of her spirit,
  Fallen in the cause of the free.

Solemn the drums thrill : Death august and royal
   Sings sorrow up into immortal spheres.
There is music in the midst of desolation
   And a glory that shines upon our tears.

They went with songs to the battle, they were young,
   Straight of limb, true of eye, steady and aglow.   10
They were staunch to the end against odds uncounted,
   They fell with their faces to the foe.

They shall grow not old, as we that are left grow old :
   Age shall not weary them, nor the years condemn.
At the going down of the sun and in the morning
   We will remember them.

They mingle not with their laughing comrades again ;
   They sit no more at familiar tables of home ;
They have no lot in our labour of the day-time :
   They sleep beyond England's foam.   20

But where our desires are and our hopes profound,
   Felt as a well-spring that is hidden from sight,
To the innermost heart of their own land they are known
   As the stars are known to the Night ;

As the stars that shall be bright when we are dust
   Moving in marches upon the heavenly plain,
As the stars that are starry in the time of our darkness,
   To the end, to the end, they remain.

LAURENCE BINYON.

40.   PICARDIE [1]

THERE's a pathway through the forest in the Picardie I know,
A port where girls haul up the boats with men and fish in tow,
And the hills run down to the market town where the country-
      women go.

And behind it is the village, and the coast-line lies below,
And down the road, the dusty road, the carts ply to and fro
By the stately frieze of forest trees beyond the old Château.

There were three of us on bicycles upon the road that day ;
You wore your coat of hunting green, and vanished down the
      way.
" *Le petit Chasseur, la mère et soeur,*" we heard the women say.

You vanished as a speck of green among the shadows blue, 10
And children trudging up the hill stood still and called to you:
" *Le petit Chasseur, qui n'a pas peur,*" they laughed and called
      to you.

O boys, you wield the bayonet now and lift the soldier's load !
O girls, you've learnt to drive the plough and use the bullock-
      goad !
But the hunter's laid, still unafraid, near the trodden Bethune
      road.

There's a pathway through the forest in the Picardie I know,
And O I'll dream and wander there ; and poppy fields will
      glow ;
And I'll watch the glare of the dusty air where the market
      wagons go.

                              ALYS FANE TROTTER.

[1] Written by the mother of a Clifton boy, Lieut. A. N. Trotter,
who was killed in the first October of the Great War, 1914, near
Bethune. She recalls a holiday he had spent with her in the same
region when he was a boy of fourteen (1908).

41.   HAPPY IS ENGLAND NOW

THERE is not anything more wonderful
Than a great people moving towards the deep
Of an unguessed and unfeared future ; nor
Is aught so dear of all held dear before
As the new passion stirring in their veins
When the destroying Dragon wakes from sleep.

Happy is England now, as never yet !
And though the sorrows of the slow days fret
Her faithfullest children, grief itself is proud.
Ev'n the warm beauty of this spring and summer   10
That turns to bitterness turns then to gladness,
Since for this England the beloved ones died.

Happy is England in the brave that die
For wrongs not hers and wrongs so sternly hers ;
Happy in those that give, give, and endure
The pain that never the new years may cure ;
Happy in all her dark woods, green fields, towns,
Her hills and rivers and her chafing sea.

Whate'er was dear before is dearer now.
There's not a bird singing upon his bough   20
But sings the sweeter in our English ears :
There's not a nobleness of heart, hand, brain
But shines the purer ; happiest is England now
In those that fight, and watch with pride and tears.

                                        JOHN FREEMAN.

42.   SONNET

THERE was an Indian, who had known no change,
     Who strayed content along a sunlit beach
Gathering shells.   He heard a sudden strange
     Commingled noise : looked up ; and gasped for speech.
For in the bay, where nothing was before,
     Moved on the sea, by magic, huge canoes,
With bellying cloths on poles, and not one oar,
     And fluttering coloured signs and clambering crews.

And he, in fear, this naked man alone,
     His fallen hands forgetting all their shells,   10
His lips gone pale, knelt low behind a stone,
     And stared, and saw, and did not understand,
Columbus's doom-burdened caravels [1]
     Slant to the shore, and all their seamen land.

                           J. C. SQUIRE.

43.   THE SNARE

I HEAR a sudden cry of pain !
     There is a rabbit in a snare :
Now I hear the cry again,
     But I cannot tell from where.

But I cannot tell from where
     He is calling out for aid ;
Crying on the frightened air,
     Making everything afraid.

Making everything afraid,
     Wrinkling up his little face,   10
As he cries again for aid ;
     And I cannot find the place !

         [1] light sailing-vessels.

And I cannot find the place
　　Where his paw is in the snare :
Little one ! Oh, little one !
　　I am searching everywhere.

JAMES STEPHENS.

44.　　　　　　SHELLEY'S SKYLARK

(*The neighbourhood of Leghorn : March*, 1887)

SOMEWHERE afield here something lies
In Earth's oblivious eyeless trust
That moved a poet to prophecies—
A pinch of unseen, unguarded dust :

The dust of the lark that Shelley heard,
And made immortal through times to be ;—
Though it only lived like another bird,
And knew not its immortality :

Lived its meek life ; then, one day, fell—
A little ball of feather and bone ;　　　　　10
And how it perished, when piped farewell,
And where it wastes, are alike unknown.

Maybe it rests in the loam I view,
Maybe it throbs in a myrtle's green,
Maybe it sleeps in the coming hue
Of a grape on the slopes of yon inland scene.

Go find it, faeries, go and find
That tiny pinch of priceless dust,
And bring a casket silver-lined,
And framed of gold that gems encrust ;　　　　20

And we will lay it safe therein,
And consecrate it to endless time ;
For it inspired a bard to win
Ecstatic heights in thought and rhyme.

THOMAS HARDY.

45.   THE DARKLING THRUSH

I LEANT upon a coppice gate
  When Frost was spectre-gray,
And Winter's dregs made desolate
  The weakening eye of day.
The tangled bine-stems scored the sky
  Like strings of broken lyres,
And all mankind that haunted nigh
  Had sought their household fires.

The land's sharp features seemed to be
  The Century's corpse outleant,   10
His crypt the cloudy canopy,
  The wind his death-lament.
The ancient pulse of germ and birth
  Was shrunken hard and dry,
And every spirit upon earth
  Seemed fervourless as I.

At once a voice arose among
  The bleak twigs overhead
In a full-hearted evensong
  Of joy illimited ;   20
An aged thrush, frail, gaunt, and small,
  In blast-beruffled plume,
Had chosen thus to fling his soul
  Upon the growing gloom.

So little cause for carollings
  Of such ecstatic sound
Was written on terrestrial things
  Afar or nigh around,
That I could think there trembled through
  His happy good-night air   30
Some blessed Hope, whereof he knew
  And I was unaware.

                    THOMAS HARDY.

46.   THE ROSE-MIRACLE

" And therefore is that Feld clept the Feld of God Floryssched : for it was fulle of Roses "—SIR JOHN MAUNDEVILLE.

I WATCHED the alleys of the garden fill
   With drift of rose-leaves by the soft South shed
   In sweet Midsummer, while I sat and read
From the quaint book of old John Maundeville.
And there I found this tale that haunts me still :
   " Falsely accused, by foes encompassed,
   A guiltless maid of Bethlehem was led
Forth from the town to die on Flourisht hill.

But while they lit the faggots she made prayer
   To her dear Lord : and straightway all were ware   10
   Of a strange stillness smiting them with awe ;
And lo, red roses where the faggots burned,
And unburned boughs into white rose-trees turned :
   Now these were the first roses that men saw."

                                ANON.

47.   " I VOW TO THEE, MY COUNTRY "

I vow to thee, my country—all earthly things above—
Entire and whole and perfect, the service of my love,
The love that asks no questions : the love that stands the test,
That lays upon the altar the dearest and the best :
The love that never falters, the love that pays the price,
The love that makes undaunted the final sacrifice.

And there's another country, I've heard of long ago—
Most dear to them that love her, most great to them that
   know—
We may not count her armies : we may not see her king—
Her fortress is a faithful heart, her pride is suffering—   10
And soul by soul and silently her shining bounds increase,
And her ways are ways of gentleness and all her paths are
   peace.   CECIL SPRING-RICE.

EXERCISES

1. FLANNAN ISLE

1. How does the poet emphasise the unnatural and mysterious character of Flannan Isle ?

2. Quote lines from this poem in which the poet has written of familiar and commonplace things. Do you think they add to the beauty of the poem ?

3. At the end of the poem there is a reference to the curse that lay on the keepers of the lighthouse. Tell any other such legend of the sea.

4. You have read Coleridge's *The Ancient Mariner*. Are there any ways in which this poem reminds you of it ?

5. The last lines of a poem are most important and must be particularly effective. What can you say about the last two lines of this ?

6. Write a brief note on the riming and stanza-scheme of this poem.

2. THE BALLAD OF KING HJÖRWARD'S DEATH

1. Write short notes on (a) Odin, (b) Valhalla, (c) Asgard.

2. What happened to King Hjörward, according to this poem ?

3. What is the general meaning of the last six stanzas ?

4. Choose and quote passages which give a vivid description of nature and the sea. Write any note you think desirable on the passages you choose.

5. Imagine yourself a Viking of old. Write a descriptive passage concerning your mode of life.

6. The Ballad is sometimes described as the poem of the half-told tale. Would you call this poem a ballad in the real sense ?

7. Try to write a stanza of your own with the rhythm and rime-scheme of this poem.

3. THOBAL

1. This is a story-poem with a lesson attached. Do you think the moral spoils the poem ?

2. " Thy gospel is the counter and the till." What exactly does this mean ? Quote a saying attributed to Napoleon which has the same meaning.

3. Imagine that someone has criticised this poem as being militarist in tone. Write your answer to this criticism.

4. Compare this poem with Sir Henry Newbolt's *Vitaï Lampada* (" There's a breathless hush in the Close to-night "). Which do you prefer, and why ?

5. Relate any incident you have read or heard of during the Great War that would make a suitable theme for a poem of this type.

4. THE SONG OF THE FIXTURE CARD

1. What is the purpose of the Introductory lines to the Song ? Write a criticism of them as poetry.

2. Do you think the description of a game such as football or cricket is better in poetry than in prose ? Use this poem and any other you happen to know on the subject as illustrations for your argument.

3. This poem was written during the Great War. What (*a*) direct, (*b*) indirect evidence is there of this in the poem ?

4. This piece is entitled a *Song*. Do you think it would go well to music ? Give detailed reasons for your answer.

5. Compare and contrast the last two stanzas of this poem with the following stanza of the famous Harrow Football Song, *Forty Years On* :

> Forty years on, growing older and older,
>   Shorter in wind, as in memory long,
> Feeble of foot, and rheumatic of shoulder,
>   What will it help you that once you were strong ?
> God give us bases to guard or beleaguer,
>   Games to play out, whether earnest or fun ;
> Fights for the fearless, and goals for the eager,
>   Twenty, and thirty, and forty years on !

6. Choose and quote (*a*) two thoughts in the poem that appeal to you ; (*b*) two passages or lines that seem to you really poetic ; (*c*) two passages or lines that seem to you somewhat prosaic.

5. THE SONG OF THE UNGIRT RUNNERS

1. What do you understand by the " atmosphere " of a poem ? Write a brief note on the atmosphere of this poem.

2. What is the purpose of the questions in the second stanza ? Do you consider them effective ?

3. What is meant by the *ungirt* runners ? How is the force of the epithet emphasised in the poem ?

4. Illustrate by quotation the repetition of thought and phrase in the poem. Write a short note of appreciation.

5. This is a poem of physical joy. Compare it in this respect with *The Song of the Fixture Card*.

6. SAN STEFANO

1. Of what poem of Tennyson does this poem remind you ? Do you think Newbolt or Tennyson has written the better poem ? Set out your reasons in full.

2. Write a short note of appreciation on the nature description in this poem.

3. Make notes on :

(*a*) word and phrase repetition in the poem ;
(*b*) the effect of the chorus ;
(*c*) the internal rimes.

4. Criticise this poem on the score of (*a*) its poetry ; (*b*) its militant spirit.

5. Write a short essay on War and Battle Poems, with special reference to the soldier- and sailor-poets of the Great War.

7. CHRISTMAS, 1903

1. Explain the title of this poem.

2. Would this poem be better or worse without its Christmas element ? Do you think the " peace and goodwill " idea an intrusion ?

3. Write a note on the Nature-pictures in this poem, referring especially to (*a*) Dawn, (*b*) the " homely " passages, (*c*) the Sea. Do you think the Nature descriptions are merely conventional ?

4. Give some examples from this poem of Mr. Masefield's use of (*a*) antithesis, (*b*) the adjective. Write brief comments.

5. Give an account of the rhythm of this poem. Point out any instance where it seems to be faltering or irregular. Are such apparent irregularities deliberate ?

8. SEA FEVER

1. This poem has been set to music. Do you consider the lyric suitable for a musical setting as a song ? If you were commissioned to set the poem to music, what would be some of the chief characteristics of your setting ?

2. Give reasons for the poet's emphasis of the wind in this poem. Is there any just criticism to be levelled at him for confusion of weather and time in his description ?

3. Name two poems and two prose books of " the vagrant gypsy life." Give some account of them, particularly in reference to this poem.

4. Poetry has been called " the music of words." How is that definition inadequate, as applied to this poem ?

9. NOMADS

1. Is there an atmosphere of wideness and freedom in this poem ? Justify your answer, and refer to *Sea Fever*.

2. Does this poem reflect the *merchandise* or the *magic* of the East ?

3. Give instances of (a) word-repetition, (b) faulty rhythm, (c) alliteration, in the poem. Discuss their effectiveness.

4. What do you consider (a) the most musical, (b) the most dignified, passage in the poem ? Do you think the ending effective ?

10. MIRAGE

1. This poem is both *moral* and *descriptive*. Can you trace and recognise these two characteristics ?

2. How does the poet emphasise the greed of the merchant and the spite of the camels ? Is this emphasis really effective ?

3. Give a short appreciation of the descriptions of (a) the various animals mentioned in the poem ; (b) the scene in the camp at night, with the men sleeping ; (c) the dream-city.

4. Quote passages to show how the poet has introduced *colour* into the poem.

5. Write a note on the use of proper names in this poem and in *Nomads*.

6. What is the theme of the song introduced into the poem ? For what purpose is the song introduced ?

7. Describe (a) the rime ; (b) the rhythm, of this poem. Write a note of appreciation.

11. THE MARINERS

1. Would it be easy for an artist to paint such a picture as is described here ?   Mention some characteristics of such an imaginary picture.   Is there any actual place you know that reminds you of this scene ?

2. Select and quote passages from the poem in which the sea is likened to a beast. Is such a simile natural ? Write other metaphors and similes connected with the sea both in storm and in calm weather.

3. What natural contrast could you make between this poem and *Christmas* 1903 (No. 7) ? Are poems of " sea-sorrow " more common in literature than poems of sea-joy ? Give a reason with your answer.

4. The following sea-poems might be compared with *The Mariners* : Kingsley's *The Three Fishers* ; Tennyson's *Break, break, break* ; Arnold's *The Forsaken Merman*. Read these poems and attempt a comparison.

5. How has the poet tried to depict the hardness and grimness of Nature ?   Has she succeeded ?

6. Show in a short note how the stanzas of this poem are constructed.   Do you think the stanza-construction a good one ?

12. THE WEST WIND

1. Choose from this poem a number of (*a*) words, (*b*) phrases, that seem to you essentially poetical or musical.

2. Who wrote a famous *Ode to the West Wind* ? In what essential does it differ from this poem ? Can you explain that difference ?

3. Write a note on :

(*a*) the effectiveness of the address of the wind to the exile ;

(*b*) the use of the word " brother " in that address.

4. How does the appeal of the west wind differ from the appeal of the sea in *Sea Fever* (No. 8) ? Do you think these poems sincere ?

5. Attempt a stanza, modelled on Mr. Masefield's (cp. also Nos. 7 and 8), on the same theme as is treated in this poem.

6. What particular aspect of Nature might appear in a poem about (*a*) the South Country ; (*b*) the North Country ; (*c*) East Anglia ; (*d*) Wales ; (*e*) London ?

13. HOLIDAY

1. Make a list of the expressive verbs in this little poem, and write a short note of appreciation on their use.

2. Is the note of this poem grave or gay ? Give your reasons. Make some comment on the suitability of the title.

3. Write a sincere paragraph, actually descriptive of a holiday of your own, somewhat on the lines of this poem.

4. Do you detect any irregularity of rhythmic movement in the poem ? Is it deliberate ?

14. HE DOES NOT DIE

1. In what season of the year do you imagine this poem to have been written ? Justify your imagination, as well as you can.

2. Give this poem a " philosophical " title, and set down its philosophy in a compact and dignified prose paragraph. [N.B.— a paraphrase is not wanted.]

3. Interpret the meaning and significance of the passages : (a) the spring's superb adventure ; (b) his loud October sky ; (c) for native ghosts return ; (d) though myself be crosst The shuddering of that dreadful day.

4. This poem occurs at the end of Mr. Hilaire Belloc's prose " Farrago " on Sussex, called The Four Men. Can you imagine something of the nature and character of that book ?

5. The stanza-form in this poem is quite regular and conventional. Is there any special reason for this ?

15. IN ROMNEY MARSH

1. Is there a good representation of sound in this poem ? In your answer make definite reference to any passages or phrases that are relevant.

2. What could you say of the colour in the poem ? Is it over-done ? Mention any peculiarity that strikes you in connection with some of the colour words.

3. Write your criticism or your appreciation of the sunset description in the poem. Compare it with any other famous sunset of literature that you happen to know.

4. Uphold or oppose the argument that

> " And roses filled Heaven's central gates "

and   " The beach, with all its organ stops
                   Pealing again, prolonged the roar "

are the worst and the best passages respectively in the poem.

5. Give some examples of alliteration from the poem. Is it effective ?

16. ESSEX

1. The author of this poem is a missionary in Africa. Is there anything autobiographical in the poem ?

2. Do you think the use of proper names in this poem effective ? Make a list of beautiful place-names known to you that you would like to use in a poem.

3. Compare this poem with *He does not die* (No. 14). Is there any hint in the two poems that Sussex is a land of hills and downs, while Essex is a flat county ?

4. Comment on the rime-scheme of the stanzas. Is there any reason for there being only a single rime-set in each stanza ? How would you describe the endings of the unrimed lines ?

17. GIBRALTAR

1. Compare this poem with *Christmas, 1903* (No. 7) in thought and idea. How do the two poets differ in their treatment of the subject ?

2. Would it be true to say that this poem lacks imagination ? What do you consider to be the best passage of real poetry in it ? Give your reasons.

3. What is a sonnet ? Give some account of the various types of sonnet. What reasons can you give for and against including this poem among sonnets ?

4. If you were making an anthology of patriotic poems would you include *Gibraltar* ?

18. A CINQUE PORT

1. The theme of this poem is the Changes wrought by Time. Mention any other poems you know in English with the same theme, and make some comparisons. Is the subject worthily treated here ?

2. Why has the poet emphasised the element of war and battle in the contrast he is making between the Cinque Port and the stranded town ? Try to fix the name of the town referred to, and interpret the references.

3. Write a short descriptive paragraph, remembering this poem and *In Romney Marsh* (No. 15), entitled Seaside.

4. Make a definite comparison of this poem with No. 15 under the headings (a) Subject, (b) Atmosphere, (c) Style or Treatment.

5. Is the internal rime in this poem a success ? Have you any criticism of the stanza-form ?

19. PAN

1. Who was Pan ? Write a brief essay on Nature Personification.

2. Make a note on the blending of the real and the fanciful in this poem. Is the description of the gutter-child true in its detail ?

20. THE ANCIENT FAITH

1. Write a brief essay on *The Fairy Element in Nature*, using for illustration this and any other poems you know on the subject.

2. How does this poem differ from an ordinary Nature poem ? Is it more or less effective ? Does the actual nature description suffer by the introduction of the fairy element ?

3. Is the poet's indictment of modern " faithless pride " perfectly justified ? Answer with some reference to this poem and to *Pan* (No. 19).

21. MARSH MARIGOLDS

1. Comment upon the use of adjectives in this poem. Are the adjectives used distinctive or picturesque ? Do you think there is an excess of adjectives ?

2. In what respect is the nature of this poem unfamiliar ? In your answer quote or mention some other April poems you know.

3. Is the attempt at (a) creating an atmosphere, (b) painting word-pictures, successful in this poem ? Give quotations in illustration of your answer.

22. THE THISTLE

1. Write an appreciation of this poem as a bit of Nature realism. What kind of picture would best represent the poet's description ?

2. Try to interpret the two lines :
> " From the sky comes no laughter,
> From earth not a moan "

as they stand in the poem.

3. Do you think the end of the poem effective ? Give your reasons.

4. Contrast this poem with *Marsh Marigolds* (No. 21).

5. Is there any moral inferred in the poem ?

6. Do you think the peculiarity of expression and rhythm in this poem deliberate ? If so, why ?

23. TO A THRUSH

1. Which stanza do you like best ? Give reasons.

2. Does Shakespeare come naturally into this poem ? Write your own opinion in a short paragraph.

3. In what way is the thrush of this poem like the same author's marsh marigolds (No. 21) ? What aspect of Nature do you think appeals most strongly to the author ?

4. How far is this poem a poem on love of England ? How is such love emphasised ? What famous poet praised the beauty of " our little England " in contrast to " far-off landscapes lit with sunnier glow," and brought a thrush into his poem ? Quote the famous passage in the poem about the thrush.

5. " This poem displays a Wordsworthian attitude to Nature." Explain this statement.

24. THE THRUSH

1. How does this poem differ in thought and treatment from *To a Thrush* (No. 23) ? Which in your opinion is the greater poem ?

2. Make a note upon :

    (a) the realism in the description of the town ;

    (b) the emphasis of the silence before the thrush's song ;

    (c) the position of the listener in the poem—*e.g.* why has the poet not used the first person ?

3. Give in your own prose (so far as prose will express it) the general sense of :

    (a) " And the cool furled bud . . . eternity in the heart " ;

    (b) " O harp from which . . . at the summons of a bird."

4. The descriptive colouring in the opening and the ecstatic address at the ending have been criticised as excessive. Discuss or reply to this criticism.

5. Make a note on the effect of the feminine rimes in the poem, quoting to illustrate your note.

6. Write a short essay on " Bird Poems in English."

25. TIME, YOU OLD GIPSY MAN

1. Who is the speaker in this poem ? Is the poem a child's question ?

2. In what respects does the personification of Time in this poem differ from the conventional personification ? Why is the picture of Time as a gipsy particularly suggestive ? Is the gipsy idea consistent throughout the poem ?

3. How is the second of the long stanzas a deep reflection on history ? Is the reference to London prophetic ? Explain the lines " Under Paul's dial You tighten your rein."

4. Do the rhythm and metrical form add effectiveness to the thought ? Does the repetition of the opening request make a good and fitting ending ?

26. THE LAKE ISLE OF INNISFREE

1. Illustrate from these lines the poet's sense of colour and sound.

2. Compare the sense of exile in this poem with that revealed in *Essex* (No. 16). Give an example of any other poem of home-sickness.

3. How far is the effect of this poem aided by alliteration, onomatopœia, repetition ? Do you think such aid merely artificial ?

27. THE DREAM-CHILD'S INVITATION

1. Interpret the title of this poem. What is its setting ? Who is the speaker ?

2. Comment on and appreciate the skill with which the various legends of long ago are introduced. Does the reference to the story of Bethlehem add to or detract from the effect ?

3. Quote examples of picturesque expression like " where clouds are scattering diamonds down on every cottage window-pane."

4. What elements in the poem have gone to make up the general dream effect ? Make some classification of these elements.

5. Make a note on the general construction of the poem under these headings : (*a*) stanza-form ; (*b*) rhythm ; (*c*) the italicised pieces ; (*d*) the use of parenthesis.

28. PINK ALMOND

1. Compare the subject with that of *Marsh Marigolds* (No. 21). Is this poem better or worse for being without a moral ?

2. Discuss the comparison of the almond blossom to stars, roses and snowflakes.

3. Add a stanza to the poem, *or* write two or three stanzas like these, called *White Cherry*.

29. "SPRING GOETH ALL IN WHITE"

1. Is there a picture in this poem ? If so, try to describe it in your own prose.

2. Compare or contrast the treatment of Spring in some other poem—*e.g.* in these lines from Mr. A. E. Housman's *A Shropshire Lad* :

> "Loveliest of trees the cherry now
> Is hung with bloom along the bough,
> And stands about the woodland ride,
> Wearing white for Eastertide."

30. A LEAF ON THE WATER

1. Write a brief note of appreciation on the references to the various seasons. Is the general atmosphere of the poem sad or happy, of Autumn or of Spring ?

2. Imagine that you had to illustrate this poem for a Child's Gift-book. What would you put into the picture ? Give some description of your illustration, or make the actual drawing if you can.

3. Make some comments on, and quote passages to illustrate, the felicities of expression in this poem. In what ways is the metrical form suited to the thought and expression ?

4. Write a note on the handling of the metaphor of the ship.

31. CARGOES

1. In what way is this poem a revelation of national or regional characteristics ? How can you tell that Mr. Masefield's affection is with the "dirty British coaster" ?

2. Give some appreciation of the poet's skill in differentiation in the three stanzas : *e.g.* "Quinquireme ... rowing " ; " galleon ... dipping " ; " coaster ... butting."

4. Write a note on " the poetry of names," referring particularly to the last stanza with its common things and ugly names. Contrast the last stanza with Rupert Brooke's *The Great Lover* : " These I have loved."

4. Write a note on the stanza-form of the poem, with special reference to the riming.

5. Write a short paragraph on " Mr. Masefield as a Poet of the Sea." Refer to his other poems in this book.

32. A SAXON SONG

1. Express the theme of this poem in a simple paragraph of your own called *The Saxon*.

2. Is this poem justly entitled a *Song* ? Would it go well to music ? (In your answer, remember that No. 31 has been set to music.)

3. What aspects of (a) Nature, (b) Man, (c) Patriotism, are revealed in this poem ?

4. What words are there in this poem definitely of Latin origin ? Make some comment on your finding.

5. Compare this poem with *Mirage* (No. 10) in its atmosphere. How are East and West contrasted by the writer ? Has she succeeded in her contrast ?

33. THE BRIDGE

1. Appreciate the various descriptions, under the following definite heads : (a) the signal ; (b) the track ; (c) the oncoming train.

2. Quote passages to illustrate the poet's sense of *sound*. Does he make any use of onomatopœia ? If not, how does he get his effects ?

3. How does the poet emphasise the idea of *night* and *dark* ?

4. Write brief notes on : (a) Nature in the poem ; (b) the similes ; (c) the personification.

5. Read Dickens's account of a train journey in *Dombey and Son*, ch. 20, along with this poem. What comparison can you make ?

6. How does a railway compare as a poetic subject with the motor-car ? with the aeroplane ? with the bicycle ?

34. THE BULL

1. Would this poem be as effective in an English (instead of a tropical) setting ? Give your reasons.

2. Write a note in appreciation of the description of the various animals in the poem. Make particular comment on the verbs and adjectives used.

3. Tennyson wrote of " Nature red in tooth and claw." How does *The Bull* illustrate this thought ?

4. Read two or three of the stories in Kipling's *First Jungle Book*. How does this poem differ from that book in its attitude to wild Nature ?

5. Give illustrations of repetition in the poem. What effects are sought by it ?

35. LULLABY

1. What is a Lullaby ? Does this poem conform to the ordinary lullaby style and idea ? Mention some other lullabies you know in literature, and make some comparison with this poem.

2. Write notes on :
   (a) the symmetry of the stanzas ;
   (b) vowel-music in the poem.

36. THE HUNTER

1. Why is this poem called *The Hunter* ? What is the quarry ? Is the hunter successful in his hunting ?

2. What do you understand by Yucatan ? Is it actual or only a dream ? Do you think there is any symbolism or parable in the poem ?

3. Coleridge dreamed and wrote *Kubla Khan* after reading the story in a book. With special reference to stanza 3, compare the two poems generally.

4. " The atmosphere of this poem is tropical." Comment on this remark.

5. Write notes on :
   (a) the proper names in stanza 1 [cp. No. 31];
   (b) the final line of each stanza ;
   (c) adjectives and verbs in the poem :
   (d) stanza 5.

37. NOD

1. What is the prevailing atmosphere ? How is it obtained and sustained ?

2. Who is Nod ? Write a note in appreciation of the poet's blending of actuality and fancy.

3. Give instances of the perfect use of vowel-sound in this poem. Add a note on the vocabulary in general.

4. How does the natural setting differ from the realism of a poem like *The Thistle* (No. 22) ? Would you imagine Mr. de la Mare to be a countryman or a townsman ?

5. Is there any characterisation in this poem ? Are Nod and Slumber-soon merely dream characters, or do they seem real to you ? Why does the poet make them so old ?

6. Do you think the poem would be improved or spoiled by the addition of feminine rimes in the first and third lines of each stanza ?

38. SAILING OF THE *GLORY*

1. How is the contrast of merriment and grief emphasised ?

2. What is the exact interpretation of the last stanza ? Do you think the ending natural and effective ? How would you expect the poem to end ?

3. Is there any real " sea-atmosphere " about this poem, or do you think the interest is on the land ? Compare it in this respect with Mr. Masefield's poems in this book.

4. Make some comparison of this poem with *The Mariners* (No. 11) in subject and treatment.

5. Write a note on the rime-scheme and stanza-form.

39. FOR THE FALLEN

1. What would you imagine to be the " scene " of the first two stanzas ? Do you think this poem will date itself if it survives in the years to come ?

2. How do the last two stanzas differ from the rest of the poem ?

3. Write a note on the introduction of the homely and familiar things into the pomp and dignity of this poem.

4. Which stanza of this poem has been often quoted on war memorials and at war memorial services ? Put beside it (*a*) a passage from Rupert Brooke's poems, (*b*) a passage from the Bible, that are used in the same way, and compare the three passages.

5. Write notes on :
   (a) the language ;
   (b) the irregularity of rhythm.

40. PICARDIE

1. Virgil wrote of *lacrimae rerum,* " the tears shed for human fortunes." In what ways is that idea revealed in this poem ?

2. What is the effect of the use of the French in this poem ? How is it echoed in the English ? Is there any likeness to R. L. Stevenson's *Requiem* ?

3. What is the difference in spirit between this poem and No. 39 ? Do you think you could detect such a difference without the aid of the Note to No. 40 ?

41. HAPPY IS ENGLAND NOW

1. When do you think this poem was written ? Do you agree with its main thought ?

2. Give some appreciation of the naturalism of this poem. Why is that so conspicuous an element in the poetry of the Great War ?

3. Write notes on :
   (a) the dignity of the language ;
   (b) the irregularity of the riming.

4. Make a detailed comparison of Nos. 39, 40 and 41.

42. SONNET

1. Is there any reason why this poem should have no real title ? Suggest a title for it, and give reasons for your suggestion.

2. Comment on the picture of primitive man. Is it natural ? In what way is it especially effective ?

3. Write imaginative prose passages on :
   (a) Caliban watches the coming of the boat conveying Prospero and Miranda to his island.
   (b) A savage of to-day sees an aeroplane descending over his home.

4. In what ways does this poem (a) conform to, (b) differ from, the ordinary rules for sonnet construction ? Try to explain the reasons for any departure from normal rules.

43. THE SNARE

1. Write a note on the realism of this poem. In your answer refer also to *The Bull* (No. 34) and *The Thistle* (No. 22).

2. In *Hart-leap Well* Wordsworth taught the lesson

" Never to blend our pleasure or our pride
    With sorrow of the meanest thing that feels."

Consider *The Snare* as a poem upon the same theme.

3. Mention some other poems (and prose pieces) you imagine to have been written by lovers of animals.

4. What particular device of expression do you notice in this poem ? Is it effective ?

44. SHELLEY'S SKYLARK

1. Explain the title of the poem. How does the theme of Shelley's *Ode* throw into relief the thought of this poem ?

2. What difference do you notice between the last two stanzas and the others ?

3. What is the meaning of stanza 4 ? What light does it throw on Mr. Hardy's view of Nature ? Is his view optimistic or pessimistic ?

4. Mr. Hardy's poetry is sometimes criticised as being " harsh and crude in expression, though fine in thought." Does this poem bear out the criticism ?

5. What passages in the poem do you consider especially poetic in expression ?

45. THE DARKLING THRUSH

1. Consider this poem as a description of Winter. Compare it with Shakespeare's song, " When icicles hang by the wall."

2. In his novels and poems Mr. Hardy often emphasises the hard and grim in Nature. Does the present poem exemplify this emphasis ? Can *The Bull* (No. 34) be compared with it in this respect ?

3. Contrast this poem with No. 24 in tone and treatment.

4. By what one adjective has Mr. Hardy emphasised the significance of the thrush's song ? How does it affect the thought of the poem ?

5. Compare this poem with No. 44 in expression and construction. Which poem do you prefer, and why ?

46.   THE ROSE-MIRACLE

1. Write a note of appreciation on the subtlety of the introduction of the legend into its setting in this poem.

2. Would it be true to say that this poem keeps the quaintness and simple beauty of the original ?   Give some appreciation of the poem from this point of view.

3. Read question 3 under *The Hunter* (No. 36), and extend your note to include this poem.

4. Attempt to write the legend told in this poem as a paragraph of simple and dignified prose.

5. Is the poem a true sonnet ?   Give some appreciation of the climax of its ending.

47.   I VOW TO THEE, MY COUNTRY

1. What is the interpretation of this poem ?   Do you think that the *patriotism* of the first and the *devotion* of the second stanza are well set together ?

2. Is there any Bible influence to be detected in the second stanza ?

3. Make some comparison of this poem with *Happy is England Now* (No. 41).

GENERAL QUESTIONS

1. Select the three poems of this collection that seem to you most effective. Give your reasons.

2. " Literature is a way of escape from life as well as an echo or mirror of it." Discuss this statement in connection with these Modern Poems.

3. Illustrate from the poems in this book what you consider to be the especial characteristics of the lyrical poetry of our own day.

4. Modern verse has a tendency to emphasis of realism. Illustrate this tendency from these and any other modern poems.

5. Write a note on the attitude of modern poetry to Nature. How does it differ from Tennyson's ?

6. Make some general comment on the use of rhythmical effect by modern poets.

7. " We think that, as civilisation advances, poetry must necessarily decline." Does this opinion of Macaulay (in his *Life of Milton*) seem to be borne out ?

8. " The true mission of poetry, as of all art, is to delight." Which poems in this book seem to you especially successful in this mission ? Are there any that seem to you to fail utterly ? Give your reasons.

9. " The Georgian poets ... are re-establishing the claim of familiar experiences to poetical treatment in familiar language." Discuss this dictum, with illustrations from the poems in this book.

10. " Modern poetry seems to me to be risking the loss of the quality of memorableness." Select lines from these poems that might help to rebut this criticism.

11. " Our sweetest songs are those that tell of saddest thought." From what you have gathered from these modern poems, criticise Shelley's statement.

12. " English poetry is full of the colour and odour of the sea." Illustrate this statement.

INDEX OF FIRST LINES

PRINTED IN GREAT BRITAIN BY ROBERT MACLEHOSE AND CO. LTD.
THE UNIVERSITY PRESS, GLASGOW